CW00840321

Thank you...

... for purchasing this copy of Get Ready for Year 7.

We hope that you will find this book helpful in preparing your child to move up to the next year-group. You may choose to use it during the final few months of Year 6, during the summer holidays or in the first few months of Year 7.

On our Teachers and Parents pages we summarise the likely content of each subject in Year 7. On the children's pages we feature activities that will help prepare children for the core subjects, hopefully giving them confidence to take part in their lessons with enthusiasm, skills and knowledge.

This book is part of our growing range of educational titles. Most of our books are individual workbooks but, due to popular demand, we are now introducing a greater number of photocopiable titles for teachers.

To find details of our other publications, please visit our website:

www.acblack.com

CONTENTS

Questions Frequently Asked by Parents.

With all the inevitable changes which take place along with the transfer from primary to secondary school, there may well be a few things you would like to be clear about. So, here goes with a Top 10 of questions frequently asked by parents and students who are preparing to enter Year 7:

1. Will my child be in a class or Tutor Group with their friends from primary school?

Most schools try to mix students from a variety of 'feeder' or 'partner' schools, whilst ensuring that a small number of friends are kept together within a tutor group. Teaching groups in some subjects are often formed differently, with groups of students being taught together on the basis of ability shown at primary school. This arrangement, called 'setting,' allows for movement into higher or lower sets as the year progresses, if students seem to be wrongly placed in their original set. Each school will be able to explain their policy on this.

2. What information will the secondary school have about my child?

A surprising amount of detailed information about their strengths and weaknesses, backed up by assessment results in SATs and other formal tests, together with a personal profile to which your child will almost certainly have contributed. A great deal of time will have been spent by staff from the secondary school in visiting the primary school and gathering relevant information. This is not to say that students in need of a fresh start won't get one; it's in the school's interests as much as yours to ensure that their students succeed!

3. How will I know how well my child is doing?

Communication from schools is far better now than it used to be and it would be unusual for you not to receive some form of feedback within the first term or so. This might be a brief written report indicating effort and/or attainment levels, or an opportunity to meet your child's tutor. Be aware that improvements reflected in whole National Curriculum Levels, for example from Level 4 to Level 5, are usually achieved over several terms and that your child may be working within the same Level throughout Year 7.

4. Who should I contact if problems arise?

Your first point of contact will be your child's tutor, who sees your child every day and has a pastoral responsibility for their welfare. Most problems can be resolved at this early stage, but if a matter is felt to be particularly complex or difficult to sort out, there will be a Head of Year or Head of House, to whom you can speak. Some matters relating to a specific subject may be referred to a subject teacher or Head of Department.   At the next level of seniority are Deputy Heads and the Head, who tend to deal directly with a smaller number of more serious issues.
Secondary schools are large and somewhat complicated organisations and you can probably see why it's best to channel queries via the tutor in the first instance!

5. How much help should I give with homework?

This is a difficult one. As a rule, teachers expect students to 'have a go' with their homework and will prefer a fair effort, with mistakes, rather than a perfect piece of work, which has been done by a parent. After all, teachers need to know what students haven't fully grasped in order to fill in these gaps in later lessons. By all means, help your child with their homework, but be wary of doing it for them; a note to the teacher explaining a difficulty is always appreciated and may help avoid the same problem in future. Remind your child that if they don't understand a homework, they can always ask their teacher for help.

6. What exams will my child have to do in Year 7?

There are no SATs in Year 7, which may come as a relief to you. Schools may have their own internal tests and exams and will be able to confirm this themselves.

7. Are exam results the only thing which schools are really concerned about?

No. Exam results are important and schools face enormous pressures in this respect, but they are only part of what schools are about. An equally important priority is producing rounded young people with the wide range of personal qualities, interests and skills necessary to succeed in an increasingly complex world.

8. How will I find out about the school's policy on discipline and is there a Code of Conduct?

All schools are expected to have a clear policy, which is available to parents on request. A summary is often included in the students' handbook, homework diary or planner. Arrangements for punishments such as detentions are strictly controlled and a full after school detention cannot be given without parents being informed at least 24 hours in advance.

9. How big a problem is bullying in Secondary schools?

Bullying exists, and most schools have an effective policy in dealing with it. If you suspect that your child is a victim, don't delay in making your concerns known to the school. You will receive a sympathetic hearing and the response in dealing with the problem is likely to be swift.

10. What do I do if I think during Year 7 that this school isn't right for my child?

Raise your concerns with the school before taking any drastic action or allowing your worries to grow. Many difficulties become exaggerated because of poor communication while the problem is a minor one. Talk to the school and try to resolve any problems in partnership with them. If, after trying to work things out, you are convinced that the school really isn't right, then consider which other schools might be more suitable.

During their Numeracy work in Year 7, pupils will:

✓ work with positive and negative numbers, writing them in order, adding them and subtracting them;

✓ use fractions, decimals and percentages;

✓ learn the order in which to carry out calculations involving more than one of the operations of addition, subtraction, multiplication and division;

✓ use written methods for multiplication and division, learning to extend them to two decimal places;

✓ check their calculations by estimation or by reversing the process they have followed;

✓ learn to choose methods for problem solving;

✓ use algebra to represent unknown numbers;

✓ deal with sequences;

✓ plot coordinates on a grid, according to a given rule;

✓ work with parallel lines;

✓ use angles, measuring them and finding the angles in triangles, for example;

✓ convert centimetres to metres, etc;

✓ use calibrations correctly on various measuring instruments;

✓ use range, mode, median and mean in relation to data;

✓ work with simple levels of probability.

In the next twelve pages we provide practice activities for areas of mathematics that sometimes present difficulties for children as they start secondary school. We also feature a multiplication tables practice page, as proficiency with tables can make a real difference to pupils' confidence in maths lessons.

POSITIVE AND NEGATIVE NUMBERS

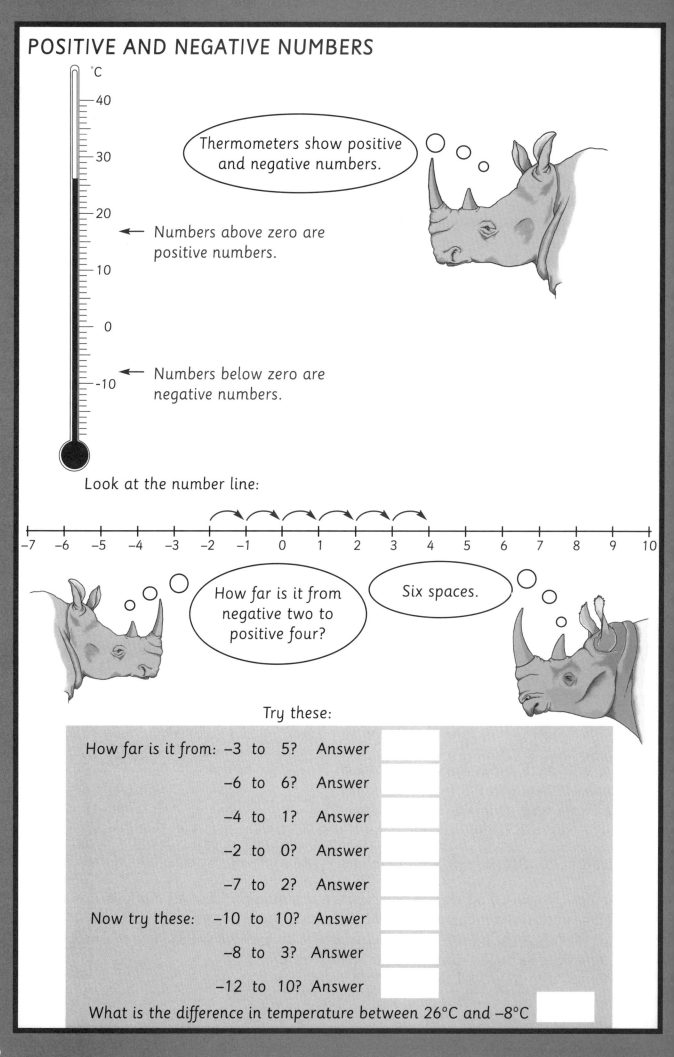

Thermometers show positive and negative numbers.

Numbers above zero are positive numbers.

Numbers below zero are negative numbers.

Look at the number line:

How far is it from negative two to positive four?

Six spaces.

Try these:

How far is it from: −3 to 5? Answer _____

−6 to 6? Answer _____

−4 to 1? Answer _____

−2 to 0? Answer _____

−7 to 2? Answer _____

Now try these: −10 to 10? Answer _____

−8 to 3? Answer _____

−12 to 10? Answer _____

What is the difference in temperature between 26°C and −8°C _____

ORDER OF OPERATIONS

Look at this question: 6 + 4 − 3

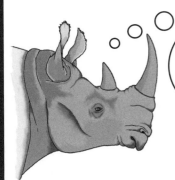

Try solving the question by doing six add four **then** subtracting three.

Try solving the question by doing four subtract three, **then** adding the answer to six.

Both ways give the same answer: 7

Now look at this question :   4 x 2 + 1

Try solving the question by doing four times two **then** adding one.

Try solving the question by doing two add one, then multiplying by the four.

The answers are **not** the same.
Only one of them is right.

This is because, in maths, we have to carry out operations in the correct order. Multiplication or division must always be completed before addition and subtraction.

So, the correct answer to the question above is 9.

Try these questions:

a. 2 + 3 x 4 = ⬚   b. 4 x 2 + 3 = ⬚

c. 18 − 2 x 3 = ⬚   d. 4 x 5 − 7 = ⬚

e. 30 − 5 x 6 = ⬚   f. 30 + 5 x 6 = ⬚

g. 8 ÷ 2 + 3 = ⬚   h. 20 + 20 ÷ 5 = ⬚

i. 32 − 48 ÷ 6 = ⬚   j. 50 − 40 ÷ 4 = ⬚

USING A PROTRACTOR - ACUTE ANGLES

Follow the steps ①, ②, ③.

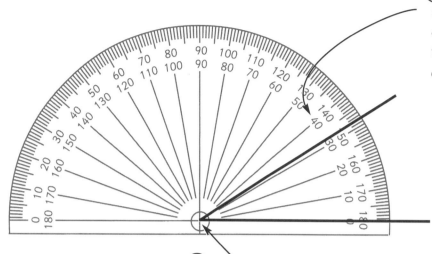

③ Remember to use the inner ring of numbers to read the size of the angle.

② This line must be matched to the zero on the <u>inner</u> ring of numbers.

① Make sure that the point of the angle matches this part of the protractor.

As you can see, this angle measures 32°.
So does the one below:

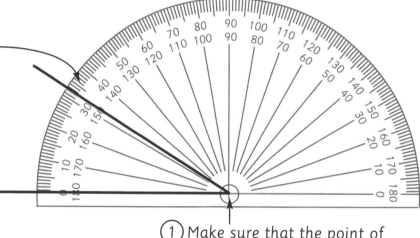

③ Read the angle from the outer ring of numbers.

② This line must be matched to the zero on the <u>outer</u> ring of numbers.

① Make sure that the point of the angle matches this part of the protractor.

Measure these angles. They are all less than 90° so we call them **acute angles**.

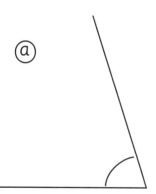

ⓐ

ⓑ

ⓒ

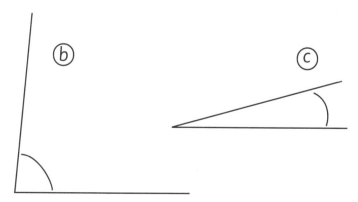

USING A PROTRACTOR - OBTUSE ANGLES

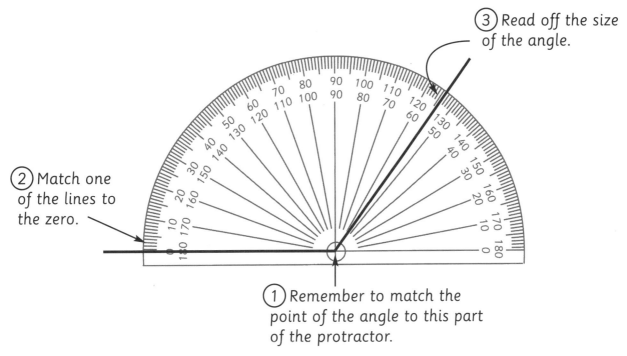

③ Read off the size of the angle.

② Match one of the lines to the zero.

① Remember to match the point of the angle to this part of the protractor.

As you can see, this angle measures 126°.
It is bigger than 90° but less than 180° so we say that it is an **obtuse angle**.

Measure the angles below. They are all bigger than 90° and less than 180°.
They are all obtuse.

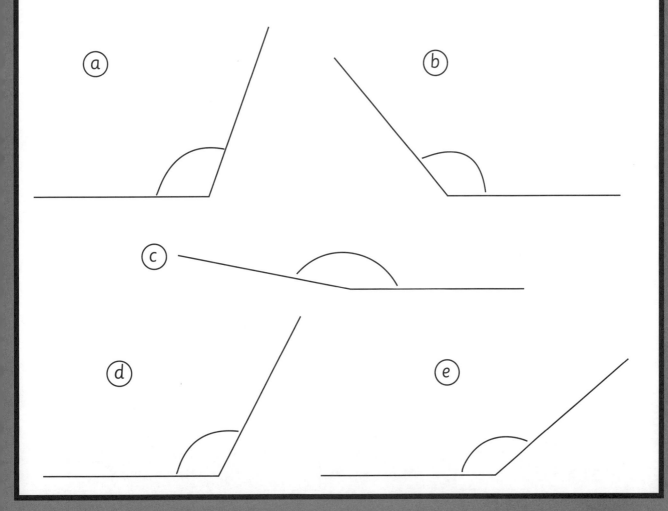

TIMES TABLES AND DIVISION

How well do you know your tables?

Time yourself completing this mixed tables square.

X	2	4	7	9	5	6	3	8
7								
3								
5								
9								
2								
8								
6								
4								

Time yourself on these sets of division questions.

Set A

a. 54 ÷ 9 =

b. 64 ÷ 8 =

c. 32 ÷ 4 =

d. 20 ÷ 5 =

e. 18 ÷ 3 =

f. 49 ÷ 7 =

g. 63 ÷ 9 =

h. 12 ÷ 6 =

i. 48 ÷ 6 =

j. 54 ÷ 6 =

Time taken

Set B

a. 18 ÷ 6 =

b. 27 ÷ 3 =

c. 36 ÷ 4 =

d. 40 ÷ 5 =

e. 81 ÷ 9 =

f. 24 ÷ 4 =

g. 16 ÷ 8 =

h. 21 ÷ 7 =

i. 100 ÷ 2 =

j. 100 ÷ 4 =

Time taken

Set C

a. 72 ÷ 8 =

b. 28 ÷ 4 =

c. 26 ÷ 2 =

d. 42 ÷ 7 =

e. 28 ÷ 2 =

f. 63 ÷ 7 =

g. 24 ÷ 2 =

h. 72 ÷ 9 =

i. 30 ÷ 2 =

j. 31 ÷ 2 =

Time taken

FRACTIONS, DECIMALS AND PERCENTAGES

A half is the same as zero point five.

And it's the same as fifty percent.

$$\frac{1}{2} = 0\cdot5 = 50\%$$

Here are some other facts to learn:

$$\frac{1}{4} = 0\cdot25 = 25\%$$

$$\frac{3}{4} = 0\cdot75 = 75\%$$

Here are some more things to learn:

Work out what needs to go in the gaps.

Fraction	Decimal	Percentage
$\frac{1}{10}$	0·1	10%
$\frac{2}{10}$	0·2	20%
$\frac{3}{10}$	0·3	30%
$\frac{4}{10}$		40%
$\frac{5}{10}$	0·5	
$\frac{6}{10}$	0·6	
$\frac{7}{10}$		70%
$\frac{8}{10}$		80%
$\frac{9}{10}$		

What fraction on the chart was worth the same as $\frac{1}{2}$? ▢

Fill in the gaps using whole numbers with decimals or fractions:

(a) $2\frac{1}{2} = 2\cdot5$

(b) $3\cdot1 = 3\frac{1}{10}$

(c) $4\cdot5 =$ ▢

(d) $6\frac{3}{10} =$ ▢

(e) $5\frac{1}{4} =$ ▢

(f) $8\cdot7 =$ ▢

FRACTIONAL PARTS

Question: What is one fifth of fifteen?

How to solve it:

$\frac{1}{5}$ of 15

The five shows that we need to split the fifteen into five parts.

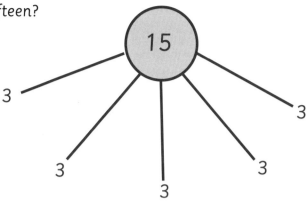

Five threes are fifteen....
....so fifteen can be split into five threes.
....so one fifth of fifteen is three.

Try these:

a $\frac{1}{4}$ of 12 = ☐ b $\frac{1}{6}$ of 24 = ☐ c $\frac{1}{7}$ of 21 = ☐

d $\frac{1}{8}$ of 48 = ☐ e $\frac{1}{9}$ of 72 = ☐ f $\frac{1}{6}$ of 42 = ☐

Question: What is four fifths of fifteen?

How to solve it:

$\frac{4}{5}$ of 15

(2) Keep four of the five parts.

(1) Split the fifteen into five parts.

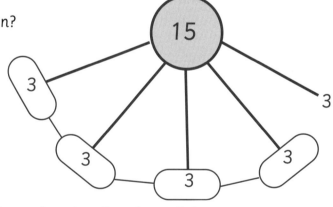

We are keeping four lots of three.

4 X 3 = 12

$\frac{4}{5}$ of 15 = 12

Try these:

g $\frac{3}{4}$ of 20 = ☐ h $\frac{2}{5}$ of 10 = ☐ i $\frac{3}{7}$ of 21 = ☐

j $\frac{2}{3}$ of 12 = ☐ k $\frac{3}{8}$ of 16 = ☐ l $\frac{5}{6}$ of 24 = ☐

12

INTRODUCING ALGEBRA

We sometimes represent an **unknown** number with a box: $6 + \boxed{} = 14$

We would work out that the value to go in the box is 8.

Try these:

(a) $5 + \boxed{} = 11$ (b) $12 + \boxed{} = 20$ (c) $7 + \boxed{} = 12$

(d) $20 - \boxed{} = 15$ (e) $30 - \boxed{} = 26$ (f) $2 \times \boxed{} = 30$

Sometimes, instead of using a box, we represent an unknown number with a letter.

If ... $6 + x = 14$

We would work out that $x = 8$

Try these:

(g) $9 + x = 14$ so $x = \boxed{}$

(h) $12 + x = 18$ so $x = \boxed{}$

(i) $22 + x = 40$ so $x = \boxed{}$

(j) $15 - x = 9$ so $x = \boxed{}$

(k) $21 - x = 17$ so $x = \boxed{}$

(l) $50 - x = 38$ so $x = \boxed{}$

Instead of writing $2 \times x$

we just write $2x$

so if $2x = 8$ we know that $x = 4$

because $2 \times 4 = 8.$

Try these:

(m) $3x = 12$ so $x = \boxed{}$

(n) $5x = 30$ so $x = \boxed{}$

(o) $2x = 26$ so $x = \boxed{}$

COORDINATES ON A GRID 1

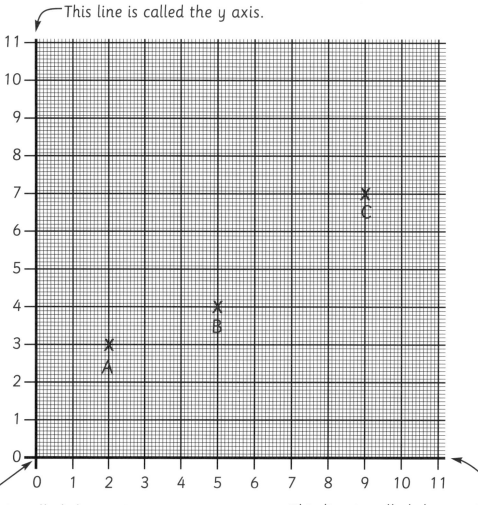

This line is called the y axis.

This point is called the origin.

This line is called the x axis.

The coordinates of point A are (2,3). Note: the x-coordinate always comes first.
At point A, $x = 2$ and $y = 3$.

At point B, $x =$ _____ and $y =$ _____
    The coordinates of point B are (,).

At point C, $x =$ _____ and $y =$ _____
    The coordinates of point C are (,).

Plot point D, where $x = 7$ and $y = 3$.

Plot point E, where $x = 4$ and $y = 6$.

Plot point F, where $x = 10$ and $y = 10$.

Plot point G, where $x = 1$ and $y = 7$.

Plot point H, where $x = 6$ and $y = 0$.

Plot point I, where $x = 8$ and $y = 8$.

Plot point J, where $x = 2$ and $y = 4$.

COORDINATES ON A GRID 2

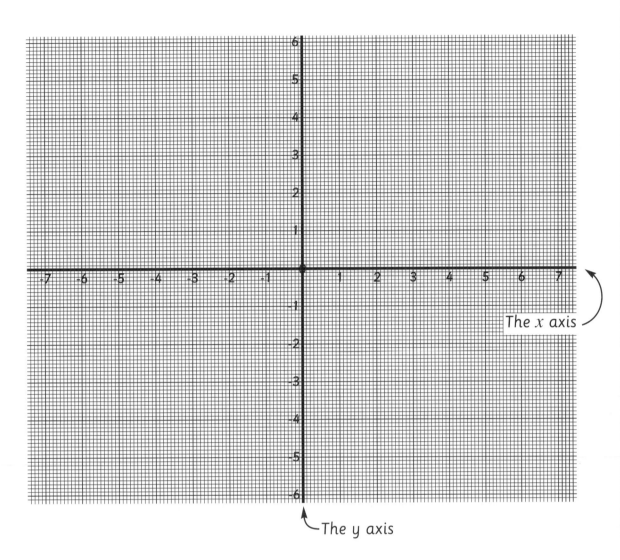

The x axis

The y axis

The grid has an *x*-axis and a y-axis but this time we are showing negative numbers as well as positive numbers. The grid now has four areas in which we can plot points. We say that it has **four quadrants**.

Plot point A where $x =$ 3 and y = 3.   (3, 3)

Plot point B where $x =$ 3 and y = –3.   (3, –3)

Plot point C where $x =$ –3 and y = –3. (–3, –3)

Plot point D where $x =$ –3 and y = 3. (–3, 3)

Join the four points to make a square.

Draw the diagonal from A to C and the diagonal from B to D.

What are the coordinates of the point where the diagonals cross?

What is the special name for this point?

HANDLING DATA

Jasdeep had a spelling test every week for nine weeks.
Here are her scores:

Week 1	Week 2	Week 3	Week 4	Week 5	Week 6	Week 7	Week 8	Week 9
7	7	6	10	9	7	9	10	7

What was her highest score? ☐

What was her lowest score? ☐

What is the difference between these scores? ☐

> The difference between the highest and lowest scores is called the range.

Which score occurred most often? ☐

> The value that appears most often is called the mode.

Write Jasdeep's scores again, going from lowest to highest:

☐ ☐ ☐ ☐ ☐ ☐ ☐ ☐ ☐

> The value in the middle,
> when the values are in order,
> is called the median.

Add all of Jasdeep's scores together ⟶ ☐

Now divide this total by the number of
tests Jasdeep had, to give ⟶ ☐

> This value is called the mean

Summary of information from this page:

range = ☐   mode = ☐   median = ☐   mean = ☐

PROBLEMS

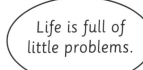

Life is full of little problems.

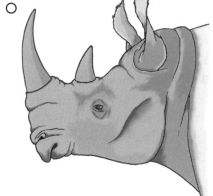

a. If I buy three bottles of lemonade for £1.25 each, how much change do I get from £5?

b. The angles of a triangle always add up to 180°. If two of the angles are 35° and 80°, what is the size of the third angle?

c. Arti buys 5 packets of balloons for a party. There are 22 balloons in each packet. How many balloons does she have altogether?

d. Arti has 25p change from £3.
What did each packet of balloons cost?

e. A new digital camera costs £320.
In a sale its price is reduced by 25%.
What is the new price?

f. How many seconds are there in ten minutes?

g. How many seconds are there in one hour?

h. A large packet of bran flakes contains 750g.
How much less than 1kg in this?

i. If I drive 128 kilometres, my car uses 16 litres of petrol.
How many kilometres per litre is this?

TEACHERS & PARENTS

During their English lessons in Year 7, your children will build on the work they have done in Year 6 and some of their lessons will be similar in structure to the primary school Literacy Hour. They will develop their vocabulary, spelling and punctuation, study non-fiction and literary texts and improve their speaking and listening skills. Children who enter Year 7 on Level 3 for English will be given support in the form of a catch-up programme. Some schools may provide literacy classes in addition to English lessons, which will usually focus on improving reading and writing skills across the curriculum.

English lessons will include work on:

✓ spelling commonly used words, including homophones (words that sound the same but are spelt differently);

✓ spelling strategies, including the use of a dictionary and spell-checker;

✓ using the apostrophe to show possession, particularly in plurals, as well as to show omission;

✓ using words precisely;

✓ making connections between words in different languages;

✓ expanding their range of link words and phrases;

✓ extending their use of complex sentences;

✓ finding information in a text using different reading skills such as skimming and highlighting;

✓ making brief notes of the key points in a text;

✓ recognising what a writer is suggesting in a text, looking beyond the surface meaning;

✓ studying use of language in creating character, setting and atmosphere;

✓ identifying the ways in which media texts (newspapers, adverts, websites) are written to appeal to a particular audience;

✓ using the appropriate terminology to comment on the ways in which writers use language (eg. metaphor, simile, alliteration, onomatopoeia);

✓ developing their personal response to texts read independently;

✓ arguing a point of view using supporting evidence;

✓ using Standard English in formal situations and in writing.

Introductory work for many of the above areas will be found in the English pages of this book.

CHOOSE THE RIGHT WORD

Homophones are words that sound the same but are spelt differently and have different meanings. Underline the correct word in each of the following sentences.

1. "Put (you're, your) coats over (their, there, they're)," said Mr. Brown.

2. James asked William (where, wear, ware) he was going.

3. The car swerved to the (write, right) and crashed into a wall.

4. Everyone went to the party (except, accept) Mandy.

5. Emily wanted to (right, write) a story.

6. The bicycle sped quickly (passed, past).

Now choose one of the words in brackets above to complete the following sentences yourself.

7. _____ dog won the pet show.

8. "I'd like you to _____ this prize," said the Headteacher.

9. "I want to _____ trainers to school," moaned Julie.

10. Mark _____ all his exams.

11. The teacher put the pile of exercise books down on _____ desk.

Here are some other words that sometimes get confused:

quite	quiet
his	he's
our	are

Underline the correct word in each of the following sentences.

12. The teacher asked the class to be (quiet, quite).

13. "When he comes back from school (his, he's) doing his homework," said Tom's Mum.

14. We (our, are) the League Champions this season.

RESPONDING TO LITERATURE 1

Read the following passage carefully. It comes from a novel called 'David Copperfield', written by Charles Dickens in the nineteenth century. In this extract, the young David Copperfield is sent away to boarding school for the first time. Don't worry if some of the words and expressions are unfamiliar at first.

'The new boy,' said the Master.

The man with the wooden leg eyed me all over – it didn't take long, for there was not much of me – and locked the gate behind us, and took out the key.

Salem House was a square brick building with wings, of a bare and unfurnished appearance. All about it was so very quiet, that I said to Mr. Mell that I supposed the boys were out. But he seemed surprised at my not knowing that it was holiday time; that all the boys were at their several homes; that Mr. Creakle, the proprietor, was down by the seaside with Mr. and Miss Creakle; and that I was sent in holiday time as a punishment for my misdoing – all of which he explained to me as we went along.

I gazed upon the schoolroom into which he took me as the most forlorn and desolate place I had ever seen. I see it now – a long room with three long rows of desks and six of forms, and bristling all round with pegs for hats and slates. Scraps of old copy books and exercises litter the dirty floor; some silkworms' houses, made of the same materials, are scattered over the desks; two miserable little white mice, left behind by their owner, are running up and down in a fusty castle made of paste-board and wire, looking in all the corners with their red eyes for anything to eat. A bird, in a cage very little bigger than himself, makes a mournful rattle now and then in hopping on his perch, two inches high, or

dropping from it, but neither sings or chirps. There is a strange unwholesome smell upon the room, like mildewed corduroys, sweet apples wanting air, and rotten books...

Mr. Mell having left me, I went softly to the upper end of the room, observing all this as I crept along. Suddenly I came upon a pasteboard placard, beautifully written, which was lying on the desk, and bore these words, 'Take care of him. He bites.'

I got up on the desk immediately, apprehensive of at least a great dog underneath; but, though I looked all around with anxious eyes, I could see nothing of him. I was still engaged in peering about when Mr. Mell came back and asked me what I did up there.
'I beg your pardon, sir,' says I; 'if you please, I'm looking for the dog.'
'Dog?' says he. 'What dog?'
'Isn't it a dog, sir?'
'Isn't what a dog?'

RESPONDING TO LITERATURE 2

'That's to be taken care of, sir – that bites?'
'No, Copperfield,' says he gravely, 'that's not a dog. That's a boy. My instructions are, Copperfield, to put this placard on your back. I am sorry to make such a beginning with you, but I must do it.'

1. Read the passage again and underline any words you do not understand. Either look them up in a dictionary or discuss their meaning with someone else.

2. Answer the following questions.
a) In the third paragraph, what do we learn about why David Copperfield had been sent to school during the holidays?

b) What did he think when he first read the placard?

c) Why do you think David had to wear the placard?

d) Find three phrases that suggest that the school was a miserable place.

e) Find three phrases that refer to one of the five senses (smell, taste, hearing, sight and touch).

3. What do you think happens when the other boys come back to school? Imagine that you are David and continue the story on a separate piece of paper.

'A line of boys marched into the schoolroom with Mr. Mell behind them. I stood there with the placard round my neck. I felt......'

WHERE DO WORDS COME FROM?

Many words in the English language come from words in Greek and Latin. You probably know that 'aqua', which is the 'root' of such words as 'aquarium' and 'aquamarine', means water. Some other common Greek and Latin 'root' words are given below, with their meanings. See if you can think of three English words which come from each 'root' word.

root	meaning			
anti	against			
astro	star			
hyper	beyond			
cent(i)	one hundred			
dia	across			
mega	many			
micro	small			
semi	half			
auto	self			
kilo	one thousand			

X	2	4	7	9	5	6	3	8
7	14	28	49	63	35	42	21	56
3	6	12	21	27	15	18	9	24
5	10	20	35	45	25	30	15	40
9	18	36	63	81	45	54	27	72
2	4	8	14	18	10	12	6	16
8	16	32	56	72	40	48	24	64
6	12	24	42	54	30	36	18	48
4	8	16	28	36	20	24	12	32

Fraction	Decimal	Percentage
$\frac{1}{10}$	0·1	10%
$\frac{2}{10}$	0·2	20%
$\frac{3}{10}$	0·3	30%
$\frac{4}{10}$	0·4	40%
$\frac{5}{10}$	0·5	50%
$\frac{6}{10}$	0·6	60%
$\frac{7}{10}$	0·7	70%
$\frac{8}{10}$	0·8	80%
$\frac{9}{10}$	0·9	90%

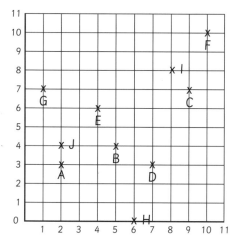

point B $x = 5$, $y = 4$ (5,4)
point C $x = 9$, $y = 7$ (9,7)

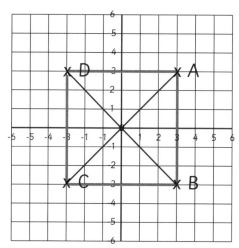

coordinates (0,0), called the point of origin.

Page 16   HANDLING DATA

highest score 10, lowest score 6
difference 4, occurred most often 7
scores in order - 6,7,7,7,7,9,9,10,10.
middle score 7, all scores together 72, mean 8.
mean 8, range 4, mode 7, median 7, mean 8.

Page 17   PROBLEMS

a.£1.25, b.65°, c.110 balloons, d.55p, e.£240,
f.600 seconds, g.3600 seconds, h.250g,
i.8 kilometres per litre.

Page 19   CHOOSE THE RIGHT WORD

1.your, there, 2.where, 3.right, 4.except, 5.write,
6.past, 7.their, 8.accept, 9.wear, 10.passed, 11.their,
12.quiet, 13.he's, 14.are.

Page 21   RESPONDING TO LITERATURE   2a.He has been sent as a punishment for a 'misdoing'. b.He thought it referred to a fierce dog. c.It seems as if he bit (or at least attacked) someone when he was at home. d.Various answers - 'a forlorn and desolate place'; any of the descriptive phrases which show the school to be messy, dirty, abandoned, etc. e.Examples: 'bristling all round with pegs for hats and slates'; 'scraps of old books and exercises litter the dirty floor' (sight); 'A bird...makes a mournful rattle now and then' (hearing); 'There is a strange unwholesome smell...like mildewed corduroys, sweet apples wanting air, and rotten books.' (smell).

3. Ask an adult to read what you have written.

Page 22   WHERE DO WORDS COME FROM?anticlockwise, antidote, antibacterial
astronomy, astrology, astronaut
hypertension, hyperactive, hypermarket
centigrade, century, centurion
diagram, diagonal, diaphragm
megaphone, megabyte, microchip
semicircle, semicolon, semidetached
automobile, automatic, autobiography
kilometre, kilogram, kilowatt

Page 23   THE APOSTROPHE

1.I had, do not, he is, here is, shall not, where is,
have not, you will, how is, was not.
hadn't, let's, isn't, weren't, she'd, can't, that's,
wouldn't.
2.The cat's coat was tangled.
The child's watch was broken.
The teacher's voice boomed across the room.
Jess and Stephanie are in a girls' football team.
The people's favourite won the competition.

Page 24	THE LANGUAGE OF NEWSPAPERS	Pun, dramatic language, rhyme, alliteration. Examples of headlines: Hounds Outfoxed! (pun) Summer Stretched for School (alliteration) Messy Nessie! (rhyme)
Page 25	FORMAL LANGUAGE	nicked - stole, dosh - money, kid - child, copper - policeman, chicken - scared, mates - friends, cheers - thank you, loads of - many/much, hang about - wait a moment, down in the dumps - depressed.

LETTER WITH INFORMAL LANGUAGE INDICATED.
Dear Mike, (first name, shortened)

Cheers (informal) for sending the tickets – (dash) I can't wait 'til (shortened word) Saturday! (exclamation mark) I still can't (shortened word) believe that Hetley are through to the semis (shortened word) – (dash) it'd (shortened word) be wicked (informal) if they got to the final. Dad's (shortened word) really (informal when used instead of 'very') excited as well, though he's (shortened word) playing Mr. Cool. (informal) Think he must be superstitious or something (shortened sentence)! (exclamation mark)

I'll (shortened word) drop you a line (informal) next week to tell you how it all went. Must dash, (informal and shortened) 'cos (shortened) Mum's (shortened) nagging (informal) me to tidy my bedroom. Typical! (shortened sentence and exclamation mark. Use of humour.)

See you

Love, (informal ending)

Eddie (shortened version of name)

EXAMPLE OF THE SAME LETTER WRITTEN FORMALLY.
Dear Mr Hadlow,

Thank you very much for sending me the tickets to the match. I can't wait until Saturday. It's hard to believe that Hetley are through to the semi-finals and it would be even better if they got to the final. My father is very excited as well, though he is pretending to be calm. I think he feels that it is bad luck to show his feelings.

I will make sure that I tell you all about the match next week. Thank you once again.

Yours sincerely,

Edward Smith

Page 26	USING DIFFERENT WORDS	excellent, beneficial, fair, delicious, luscious, useful, thorough, genuine, fine, commendable.
Page 27	EXTENDING SENTENCES	Ask an adult to read your answers.
Page 28	LINKING WORDS AND PHRASES	1.therefore, 2.firstly, 3.as a result, 4.therefore, 5.secondly, 6.so, 7.in other words, 8.for example, 9.although, 10.in fact, 11.alternatively, 12.finally.
Page 30	RENEWABLE AND NON-RENEWABLE ENERGY RESOURCES.	A-4, B-3, C-2, D-1
Page 31	ACIDS AND ALKALIS	1.very acidic - vinegar and battery acid neutral - water, slightly alkaline - soap very alkaline - oven cleaner 2.c. because neutralising the soil makes it useable so the farmer can get on with growing his crops without delay.

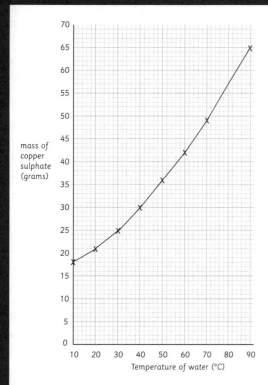

Temperature of water (°C)

Page 32   SOLUTIONS 1 AND 2
B.1.As the temperature of water rises, so does the amount of copper sulphate which dissolves. Jessica's prediction was right.
2.At 0°C the water would be frozen and no solid would dissolve. At 100°C, the water would be boiling, and therefore evaporating (turning to steam), so there wouldn't be 100g of water and it wouldn't be a fair experiment.
3.55°C, 4.Around 57g.

Page 34   SOLIDS, LIQUIDS AND GASES 1
2.gases,3.solids, 4.gases, 5.solids, 6.liquids.

Page 35   SOLIDS, LIQUIDS AND GASES 2
The key points are in the labels on the diagram. on page 34:
as ice (a solid) the particles will be very close together, vibrating and exerting a strong force; as water (a liquid) the particles will be fairly close together, moving around more and exerting some force; as steam (a gas) the particles are far apart, moving rapidly, but exerting no force on each other.

Page 36   THE SOLAR SYSTEM
Planets from left to right - Sun, Mercury, Venus, Earth, Mars,Jupiter, Saturn, Uranus, Neptune, Pluto. Gravity, Sun.

Page 39   SETTLEMENT 1
1.Positives - c, e, b. Negatives - a, d, f, g

Page 40   SETTLEMENT 2
2.Ask a friend or an adult to check this question.
3. Across 1.river, 4.market, 5.hamlet, 6.traffic, 9.train, 12.flats, 14.bike, 15.crime.
Down 2.village, 3.grow, 6.town, 7.shape, 8.cinema, 10.walk, 11.farm, 13.car

Page 41   THE ROMANS
Civilised - D, F, G, I Brutal - A, B, C, E, H

Page 42   QU'EST-CE QUE C'EST?

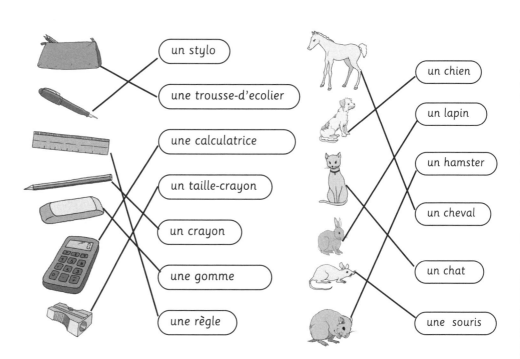

un stylo
une trousse-d'ecolier
une calculatrice
un taille-crayon
un crayon
une gomme
une règle

un chien
un lapin
un hamster
un cheval
un chat
une souris

Page 43   KEY VOCABULARY FOR YEAR 7
Hello, my name is Stephanie and I am 14 years old. I live in Paris.
Example - Bonjour! Je m'appelle Thomas et j'ai onze ans. J'habite à Wellington.

THE APOSTROPHE

Remind yourself of the different uses of this tiny punctuation mark.

1. Using the apostrophe to show omission (a letter or letters missed out).
Write out these shortened forms as two words. The first one has been done for you.

I'm =	I am	I'd =		don't =	
he's =		here's =		shan't =	
where's =		haven't =		you'll =	
how's =		wasn't =			

Write the shorter form of these words using the apostrophe. The first one has been done for you.

he will =	he'll	had not =		let us =	
is not =		were not =		she would =	
cannot =		that is =		would not =	

2. Using the apostrophe to show possession.
Remember how apostrophes are used to show when something belongs to someone.

> e.g.   The dog belonging to the boy was called Nipper.
>
>   can also be written
>
> The boy's dog was called Nipper.

If there is more than one owner, the apostrophe goes after the plural form of the noun.

> e.g.   The boys' dogs were called Nipper, Scamp and Henry.
>
>   The children's names were called out by the teacher. ('children' is the plural
> form of 'child', so the apostrophe goes after the n rather than after the s.)

Put the apostrophes into the following sentences:

The cats coat was tangled.
The childs watch was broken.
The teachers voice boomed across the room.
Jess and Stephanie are in a girls football team.
The peoples favourite won the competition.

THE LANGUAGE OF NEWSPAPERS

Newspaper reporters aim to write headlines which will grab their readers' attention. Some of the ways in which they do this are by using:

Dramatic Language - using exaggeration for effect.

e.g. **Tornado Rips the Heart From Community.**

Puns   - using words with a double meaning.

e.g. **Tornado Tears!**

(could refer to people crying
or to the tornado destroying things.)

Rhymes   - e.g. **Tale of a Gale.**

Alliteration   -using words with the same first
                letter or sound.

e.g. **Tornado Tears Through Tynemouth**

The headlines below all refer to a story about a seven year old girl who has passed Maths GCSE. Try to decide how they attract the attention of a reader.

Headline	How does it attract attention?
Sum Celebration!	
Child Genius Outsmarts Examiners	
No Strain on My Brain!	
Genius Jenny Jumps For Joy	

Read the following summaries of three stories and decide on an attention-grabbing headline for each one.

A fox outwitted hunters today when it turned on a hound and bit him on the nose before running off.

The Prime Minister has decided that school children need more holidays. He is to discuss with the government a bill to make the summer break three months long.

Scientists have gained the clearest evidence yet that the Loch Ness Monster exists. Half-eaten fish have been washed up on the shoreline.

24

FORMAL LANGUAGE

Many kinds of writing need formal language, for example essays and letters to people you don't know very well. Informal language is used more often when we speak or write to friends.

Decide whether the following words and phrases are formal or informal and write them in the appropriate column, putting words with the same meaning opposite one another.

nicked   money   kid   scared   copper   child   stole   mates

cheers   loads of   hang about   friends   down in the dumps   depressed

wait a moment   dosh   much/many   policeman   chicken   thank you

Informal		Formal	Informal		Formal
	→			→	
	→			→	
	→			→	
	→			→	
	→			→	

When writing informally, you may shorten sentences and use dashes and exclamation marks. You may shorten words (can't, won't etc.).
Read the letter below and underline or circle all the things that make it informal.

60 Lime Road,
Hetley,
Lancs.
LA7 2AT
14th June

Dear Mike,

Cheers for sending the tickets – I can't wait 'til Saturday! I still can't believe that Hetley are through to the semis – it'd be wicked if they got to the final. Dad's really excited as well, though he's playing Mr. Cool. Think he must be superstitious or something!

I'll drop you a line next week to tell you how it all went. Must dash, 'cos Mum's nagging me to tidy my bedroom. Typical!

See you

Love,
Eddie

Now try rewriting the letter in a more formal way. Imagine that Ed has been given the tickets by his Head Teacher, as a prize for leading the school football team. Remember to avoid chatty language and slang, dashes and exclamation marks. You can use some shortened words if it sounds more natural. You could begin:
Dear Mr. Hadlow,

USING DIFFERENT WORDS

Using different words makes your writing more interesting. At primary school you will have been told not to use words like 'nice' and 'good' all the time. You may even have been taught to use a thesaurus (a dictionary of word variations) to widen your vocabulary.

Here is just a small selection of words you will find if you look up 'good' (as an adjective) in a thesaurus.

> **Good**: commendable, beneficial, excellent, fine, genuine, delicious, luscious, thorough, fair, useful.

Choose the best word to fit into each of the following sentences. You may only use each word once, so you may want to use a pencil to begin with! If possible, discuss the precise meaning of each word with someone else as you do this exercise.

His school report was _____ as he gained grade A in every subject.

Taking the medicine had a _____ effect on her cold.

The teacher gave a _____ punishment to the girl who broke the window.

The cake my Dad made was _____.

_____ fruit hung from the trees in the tropical forest.

A calculator can be _____ in a Maths lesson.

She gave the horse a _____ grooming before putting him back in the stable.

The old chair we found at the dump turned out to be a _____ antique.

If the weather is _____ tomorrow we can go to the outdoor swimming pool.

The effort he put into the sponsored walk was _____ .

EXTENDING SENTENCES

'My friend has a dog.' is not a very interesting sentence.

✏ Who is the writer's friend?

✏ What does his dog look like?

Adding detail makes the sentence more interesting:

'My friend James has a black Labrador who likes to chase cats.'

Try to add detail to the following sentences. Start by asking yourself questions.
Who?   What sort?   When?   Where?   What did it look like?

1. The boy walked down the street.

2. I saw an accident.

3. The woman ran away from the man.

4. I found some money.

You probably found that you often used 'who', 'whose' and 'which' to add detail.
These words are relative pronouns. They are useful in building long sentences as they relate one part of a sentence, or clause, to another.
Eg. The girl, **whose** name was Molly, was celebrating her twelfth birthday.
    The horse **which** won the Derby was owned by a man **who** had never been to a racecourse before.
Extend the following sentences by using one or two relative pronouns.

5. In front of me stood the teacher, ...———————————————————

———————————————————————————————————————

6. I like playing with my baby cousin, ...————————

————————————————————————————————

————————————————————————————————

7. The fancy dress competition was won by Billy, ...

————————————————————————————————

————————————————————————————————————

8. If I go to the shop I pass an old house ....————————————————

——

9. Tom, ——————————————————, has a pond in his garden ....———

——

LINKING WORDS AND PHRASES

In the letter below the linking words and phrases are missing. Underline the best word or phrase from the list below.

Dear Sir,

I am writing to complain about the article in last week's 'Peesborough News' about the vandalism at the leisure centre. The writer suggested that local teenagers are responsible and that -------(1)------- the skateboarding park next to the centre should be closed at 6pm.

As a fourteen year old who uses the skateboarding park regularly, I have a number of points to make about this view. ------(2)------, there are very few things for young people to do in the area and ------(3)-------- skateboarding is very important to many of us. Most of us are very interested in the sport and -----(4)------------- would not waste our time breaking down fences or spray-painting walls. ---------(5)------, the leisure centre is floodlit until it closes at 10pm, ---(6)-------- anyone causing trouble before that time would be caught. I believe that the damage is done during the night, ----(7)------ after the skateboarders have gone home. I suggest that security around the centre is increased during these hours, -----(8)-------- by keeping the floodlights on all night. -------(9)--------- this would be expensive, it might help to catch the real vandals and would ---(10)-------save money in the long run. ----(11)--------- the police could patrol the area through the night.

----(12)--------, I would like to remind the writer that he was once a teenager himself and ask him not to label us all as criminals without evidence.

Yours faithfully

Tom Wilkinson

1. a) therefore   b) for example   c) in other words   d) by the way
2. a) secondly   b) firstly   c) thirdly   d) finally
3. a) because   b) for example   c) as a result   d) however
4. a) therefore   b) even   c) for example   d) on the other hand
5. a) firstly   b) secondly   c) thirdly   d) finally
6. a) though   b) so   c) after all   d) because
7. a) however   b) in spite of that   c) for this reason   d) in other words
8. a) for example   b) alternatively   c) in that case   d) therefore
9. a) because   b) although   c) even   d) by the way
10. a) in other words   b) otherwise   c) in fact   d) yet
11. a) by the way   b) alternatively   c) even   d) at last
12. a) secondly   b) therefore   c) finally   d) at any rate

SCIENCE is the third of the Core Subjects, and in Year 7 all students will cover a wide range of scientific topics. These are designed to build on the knowledge, understanding and skills, which students have gained in Key Stage 2.

✓ Allowance is made for students who have made more progress than the majority and for those who have performed less well. Practical work is a major feature of the course for all students.

✓ During Year 7 most students will make progress equating to about half of one National Curriculum Level. They will, therefore, end the year working in the Level 4/5 range. Some of the most important skills, which students will practise and develop, are covered in the activities in this book. These include:

✓ collecting and using data effectively;
✓ presenting results from investigations and experiments in a variety of appropriate ways, including a range of graphs;
✓ thinking skills.

Note: If your child wants to take things beyond the introductory activities, there are some extra challenges on page 37.

In their Science lessons, students can expect to experience work on:

✓ CELLS, and will learn how both animal and plant cells are structured and what they are for.
✓ REPRODUCTION, in humans and other living things. They will study the way our bodies change during adolescence and present data discovered in surveys as graphs and charts.
✓ ENVIRONMENT, and in particular the relevance of habitat for animals and plants, and the significance of feeding relationships.
✓ VARIATION AND CLASSIFICATION, amongst species of living things.
✓ ACIDS AND ALKALIS and NEUTRALISATION, learning how these qualities affect us in our daily lives. They will experiment safely with acids and alkalis, using indicators such as litmus paper to determine where on the pH scale a substance should be placed.
✓ CHEMICAL CHANGES and REACTIONS, in which they will learn to experiment safely with various chemical substances. They are likely to carry out experiments involving burning, which are designed to test whether gases are present.
✓ SOLIDS, LIQUIDS AND GASES, considering the differences between each one as explained by the PARTICLE MODEL.
✓ SOLUTIONS, in which dissolving, separation and purity are studied. For example they may experiment to produce pure salt from a piece of rock salt.
✓ RENEWABLE AND NON-RENEWABLE SOURCES OF ENERGY, and their usefulness and importance for humans and other living things.
✓ ELECTRICITY, concentrating on simple electrical circuits, which will include cel bulbs and switches. They will create simple series and parallel circuits and measure electrical currents using ammeters.
✓ FORCES, including friction, upthrust, air resistance and weight.
✓ THE SOLAR SYSTEM, and some of its phenomena, such as solar eclipses an the seasons. They will use models to explain how the earth's rotation on a tilted axis affects our daylight patterns and our seasons.

RENEWABLE AND NON-RENEWABLE ENERGY RESOURCES

Sources of energy can be sorted into two types:

NON-RENEWABLE ONES
Those that can only be used once and will eventually run out. These include gas, coal and oil, all of which are burned to release energy.

RENEWABLE ONES
Which won't run out because they continue to exist even after being used to produce energy. These include **solar** from the sun, **wave** or **tidal** power from the sea, **wind power** from the air, and **hydroelectric** from water.

Using the information above, match the halves of the sentences below.

A Wind power

1 is usually set up where water can flow downhill and turn turbines which generate electricity.

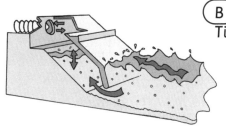

B Tidal power

2 is particularly useful in hot countries where the sun shines for long periods.

C Solar power

3 is expensive to set up because long barriers have to be stretched across the sea.

D Hydroelectric power

4 is suitable in places where there is high land and open spaces.

ACIDS AND ALKALIS

Many products we have in our houses are acids, which are quite safe for us to use.
Orange juice and vinegar are good examples.

Remember, though, some acids are extremely dangerous and you should not experiment with any which could be harmful.

You will learn to measure whether a solution is an acid or an alkali using special techniques and will use a pH scale to decide exactly how acidic or alkali each one is.

1. Use the pH scale below to put these liquids into the correct column.

vinegar pH 3   water pH 7   soap pH 8

oven cleaner pH 12   battery acid pH 1

VERY ACIDIC			SLIGHTLY ACIDIC			NEUTRAL	SLIGHTLY ALKALINE				VERY ALKALINE		
1	2	3	4	5	6	7	8	9	10	11	12	13	14

2. It is important to know that some acids and alkalis can NEUTRALISE or cancel each other out. Farmers, like Malcolm Cavill, regularly test their soils because too much acid in a soil may prevent crops from growing. Soil with a pH of around 5-7 is usually best for growing crops.

What advice would you give to Malcolm if he found that his soil had a pH of 4? Choose the best one of these answers and explain why you chose it.

a. Wait and hope that the acid gets washed away when it rains.

b. Don't plant anything in the soil for the next few years.

c. Add an alkali to the soil to neutralise it, then plant the crops, which should grow well.

d. Plant the crops and hope for the best.

SOIL
ANALYSIS
REPORT

All fields
result: pH 4

Answer: _____

because _____

_____

_____

SOLUTIONS 1

In Year 7, Jess and her friends carry out an experiment to investigate how much copper sulphate (a chemical in the form of blue crystals) would dissolve in 100g of water. They were interested to find out whether more copper sulphate would dissolve if the water was hotter.

Jess had noticed that when she put sugar into really hot tea it seemed to dissolve really quickly and easily and she predicted that more copper sulphate would dissolve in the hotter water in the experiment.

Do you think she was right?

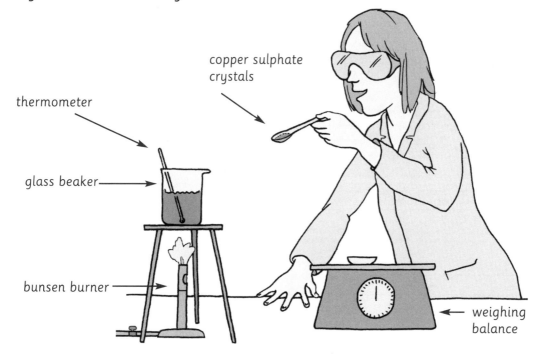

Unfortunately, Jess forgot to take a reading when the temperature of the water was 80°C, but these were the results she did get.

Temperature °C of water	Amount (mass) of copper sulphate crystals which dissolved.
10	18g
20	21g
30	25g
40	30g
50	36g
60	42g
70	49g
80	?
90	65g

SOLUTIONS 2

A. Jessica's teacher asked her to show her results on a line graph using axes like these: The first point has been plotted for you.

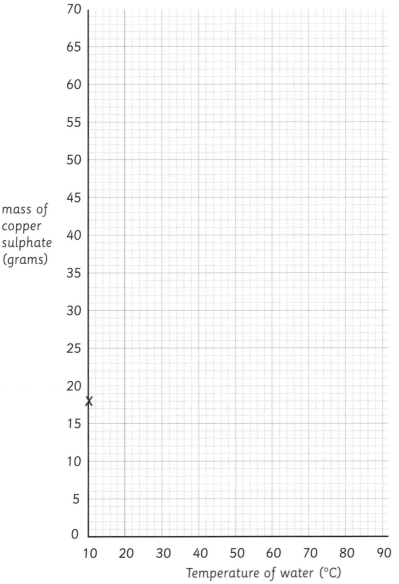

Graph to show how much copper sulphate dissolves in 100g of water at different temperatures.

mass of copper sulphate (grams)

Temperature of water (°C)

B. Use the results on your graph to answer these questions:

1.   What trend does the graph show and was Jess right?

2.   Why was it sensible for Jess not to include the temperatures 0°C and 100°C in her experiment?

3.   If you wanted to dissolve exactly 39g of copper sulphate in 100g of water, what would be the ideal temperature of water for doing so?

4.   Estimate the amount of copper sulphate that dissolved in the water at 80° C when Jess forgot to take a reading.

SOLIDS, LIQUIDS AND GASES 1

Everything around us can be classified into one of three states: SOLIDS, LIQUIDS AND GASES. All of these are made up of particles which are much too small to see, but we do know several important things about them.

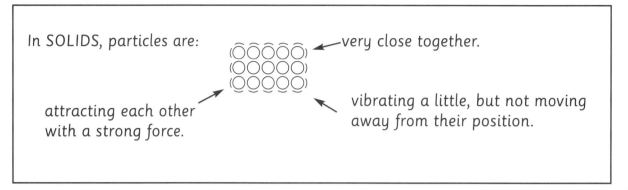

In SOLIDS, particles are: ← very close together.

attracting each other with a strong force.

← vibrating a little, but not moving away from their position.

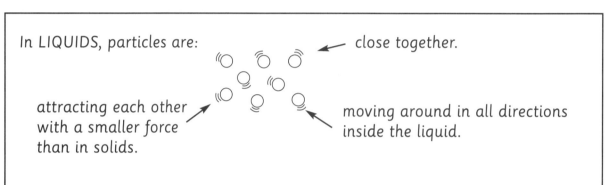

In LIQUIDS, particles are: ← close together.

attracting each other with a smaller force than in solids.

← moving around in all directions inside the liquid.

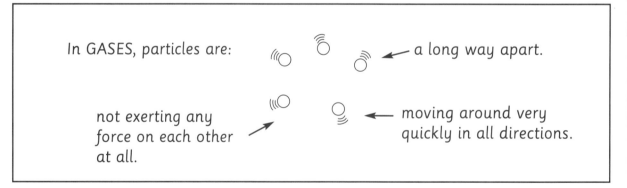

In GASES, particles are: ← a long way apart.

not exerting any force on each other at all.

← moving around very quickly in all directions.

Here is a list of facts about particles. Next to each one write SOLID, LIQUID OR GAS according to which one the description is most like. The first one has been done for you:

1.	The particles are vibrating, but not moving far.	solid
2.	The particles are moving around very quickly.	
3.	The particles are exerting a large force.	
4.	The particles are not attracting each other.	
5.	The particles are really close together.	
6.	The particles are fairly close and exerting some force.	

SOLIDS, LIQUIDS AND GASES 2

To answer this harder one you will need to apply what you know:

If you take a tray of ice cubes from a freezer the water in the tray is in SOLID form, i.e. ICE.

You leave the tray in a room for a few hours and the ice turns to water.

You could boil the water in a kettle or saucepan. Some of the water would evaporate by turning into steam.

Explain what happens to the ice/water/steam by referring to what you know about particles in SOLIDS, LIQUIDS, and GASES. Here are some phrases you might find useful:

When the ice melts the particles change from being..... ———————

_____

_____

_____

_____

In water, the particles.... ———————————————————

_____

_____

_____

_____

When the water is boiled and turned to steam.... ———————

_____

_____

_____

_____

_____

THE SOLAR SYSTEM

Read the information below about the Solar System, then add the labels for each planet shown in this diagram. To help you, the words you need are in block capitals.

The SUN is the star at the centre of the Solar System.

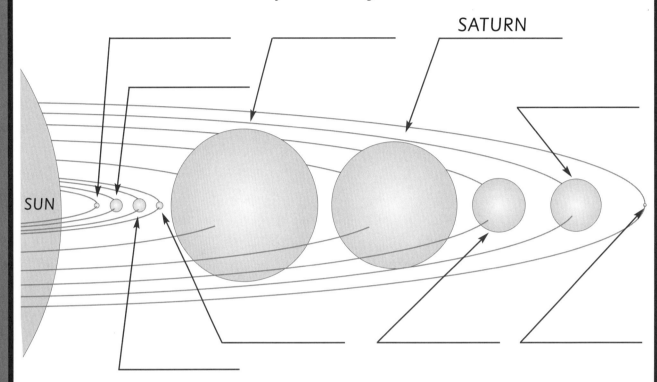

SATURN

SUN

The closest planet to the Sun is MERCURY, which is one of the two smallest ones. The smallest is PLUTO, which is the furthest away and which takes nearly 250 years to go around, or 'orbit', the Sun. The EARTH is the third planet from the Sun and its orbit takes just one year. The largest planet is JUPITER, which has MARS on one side and SATURN, the 'Ringed Planet' and second largest, on the other. URANUS and NEPTUNE are the other two, with Neptune being further away from the Sun than Uranus. VENUS is closer to the Sun than the Earth is.

So, all these planets orbit the Sun, but why don't they fly off into Outer Space? Unjumble these letters to find the missing word from the sentence below:

It's the force of the Sun's [   ] which keeps the planets in their orbits.

V A R Y T I G

An important point:

The planets themselves are not sources of light. The only sources of light are the stars. The closest star to earth is the [   ] .

ARE YOU UP FOR A CHALLENGE?

If so, try these:

1. Investigate how heavy one grain of rice is. You'll probably need to think carefully about how to work this out.

When you have worked out a way of doing this and come up with an answer, produce a set of instructions for someone else to follow in order to solve the same puzzle.

You could also try to work out how thick one page in a book is. The method would probably be based on the same idea as the rice problem.

2. Research one of the planets in our Solar System. Produce a fact sheet showing the important details about the planet – and some of the more unusual things you discover.

Did you know…?

3. If you enjoyed researching a planet, why not create one of your own?

You could do this in as much detail as you like, maybe even making a 3D model.

4. Find out about a famous scientist and produce a quiz about her or him and the work she/he did. Try out your quiz on your family or friends. Here are some well known and some less well known scientists you could research:

Sir Isaac Newton   Marie Curie   Thomas Edison   Edward Jenner

5. Research one renewable energy source (there are many useful sites on the web), and use the information you discover to write a letter to your M.P. or the Prime Minister, suggesting how more of this country's energy could be produced using this source. Make sure you mention **how** the energy is produced and what the advantages would be of this renewable source compared with the non-renewable ones.

✓ GEOGRAPHY
Students will experience work on SETTLEMENTS, including their own one, considering how and why land is used in particular ways; for housing, recreation and so on.
They will also consider why changes happen in settlements and why certain patterns of use have developed over time.
WATER may be the second major theme, with the water cycle, river features, flooding and pollution all included.
The MOVEMENT OF GOODS AND PEOPLE looks at why different forms of transport are used in different situations and how this is influenced by the landscape and by the position of settlements. The environmental impact of this movement will also be considered.

✓ History
Students are likely to study four major units or modules and will examine some key questions:

Unit 1 The Romans and their Empire. (A European Turning Point)
✏ How civilised were they and what have they left us?

Unit 2 The Medieval Monarchs. (Britain 1066 – 1500)
✏ The Norman Conquest; how did William win the Battle of Hastings and how did the Normans keep control of this country?
✏ King John: was he the most evil king England has ever had?

Unit 3 Life for the Poor in Medieval Times. (Britain 1066 – 1500)
✏ What do we know about peasants' lives and how do we know this?
✏ Why and how were wars fought in this period?
✏ What was the Black Death and why was it so significant?
✏ Why did the peasants revolt?

Unit 4 The Church and its Power : Religion and Religious Conflict
✏ In what ways was the Medieval Church powerful, and why were some people willing to die for their beliefs?
✏ Why did King Henry VIII change the Church and break with Rome?

Important skills of historical investigation will be practised and developed using a range of evidence.

✓ Modern Foreign Languages
All students will begin to study at least one Foreign Language, usually either French or German. They will be introduced to the basic vocabulary and structure of the language through 'real-life' situations. These will include meeting and greeting people, talking about themselves, their family, their homes, their pets and their interests.

SETTLEMENT 1

A settlement is a place where people live. It can be a hamlet (with just a few houses), a village, a town or a city. Which of these do you live in? There are always reasons why a settlement has developed in the way it has.

1. DIANA LIVES IN A CITY

Here are some of the things Diana says about the settlement she lives in. Put her comments into the correct column according to whether they are positive (good things) or negatives (bad things) about living in a city. The first one has been done for you.

a. Flats and houses are so expensive that I can't afford to buy one.

b. I can choose from loads of places for a night out - cinemas, clubs, theatres.

c. I love the 'buzz' here. It makes me feel really alive.

d. There's so much traffic around these days: the air smells bad all the time and it takes ages to drive anywhere.

e. When I lost my job there were plenty of other companies I could apply to, and I got another job within a few weeks.

f. My mobile phone was stolen last month and one of my friends was mugged last year.

g. Near where I live, there's a load of waste land where some factories used to be.

CITY LIFE	
Positives ✓	Negatives ✗
	a

SETTLEMENT 2

2. Something to think about:
    What's it like for young people in your settlement?
    a. I live in _____ which is a hamlet, village, town, city. Circle the correct choice.
    b. Complete the chart with your opinion by circling one of the numbers 1–10 for each aspect of life in your settlement.

	REALLY BAD				O.K.				EXCELLENT	
	1	2	3	4	5	6	7	8	9	10
Facilities for young people, like youth centres and sports clubs	1	2	3	4	5	6	7	8	9	10
Pollution	1	2	3	4	5	6	7	8	9	10
Crime/Personal safety	1	2	3	4	5	6	7	8	9	10
Shops	1	2	3	4	5	6	7	8	9	10
Litter	1	2	3	4	5	6	7	8	9	10
Vandalism	1	2	3	4	5	6	7	8	9	10
Traffic	1	2	3	4	5	6	7	8	9	10
Services, like hospitals and schools	1	2	3	4	5	6	7	8	9	10
Houses	1	2	3	4	5	6	7	8	9	10

3. Use the clues to solve the crossword. All the information is to do with settlements and the transport links between them.

ACROSS 1. Being able to cross one of these is important for settlers.
    4. Many towns and cities have one of these; people can buy and sell things here.
    5. A collection of just a few houses – smaller than a village.
    6. A major cause of pollution and congestion.
    9. Many people commute (travel) to work on these.
    12. Blocks of these were built in cities for people to live in.
    14. A two-wheeled method of travel.
    15. One of the unpleasant aspects of life in any settlement; more common in cities.

DOWN 2. Smaller than a town, but larger than a hamlet.
3. Many small settlements do this over a period of time.
6. Larger than a village, but smaller than a city.
7. The size and ………… of any settlement may change.
8. Most towns and cities have at least one of these, where people can watch films.
10. A healthy and non-polluting way to get around on foot.
11. Hamlets are often found near these; a place where crops and animals are found.
13. Most families travel between settlements in one of these motorised vehicles.

40

THE ROMANS

Read the statements below, all of which are true, then decide whether each one is evidence that the Romans were civilised or brutal. The first one has been done for you.

In the Roman Empire:

A. Slaves would be flogged regularly.

B. Criminals were executed publicly as entertainment for crowds waiting to see gladiator contests.

C. People were killed or severely punished for being Christians.

D. Magnificent examples of architecture, like the Colosseum in Rome, were built.

E. Men were allowed by law to control their wives as if they owned them.

F. Beautiful mosaics were created to decorate villas.

G. Skilful engineering was used to build roads and aqueducts.

H. Sometimes, babies were unwanted because they were female and they were left to die.

I. Houses or villas had ingenious heating and plumbing systems.

CIVILISED	BRUTAL
	A

QU'EST-CE QUE C'EST? (WHAT IS IT?)

You may need an English/French dictionary to help you with these names. Draw a line to join up the pairs.

Qu-est-ce que c'est? (What is it?)   C'est .... (It's ...)

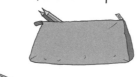

Don't forget: you'll need all these things when you start Year 7!

un stylo

une trousse-d'écolier

une calculatrice

un taille-crayon

un crayon

une gomme

une règle

Qu-est-ce que c'est?   C'est ....

It may not be such a good idea to take these things to school with you!

un chien

un lapin

un hamster

un cheval

un chat

une souris

KEY VOCABULARY FOR YEAR 7

Read through this vocabulary, then read Stephanie's speech bubble. Write a translation of what Stephanie is saying here:

_____

_____

_____

_____

_____

_____

_____

FRANCAIS	ANGLAIS
Je m'appelle	My name is
J'ai onze ans	I'm 11 years old
J'habite	I live
J'ai	I have
Une soeur	A sister
Un frère	A brother
Ma mère	My mum
Mon père	My dad
Ma grand-mère	My grandmother
Mon grand-père	My grandfather
Ma belle-mère	My stepmum
Mon beau-père	My stepdad
Ma demie-soeur	My half-sister
Mon demi-frère	My half-brother
Un chien	A dog
Un chat	A cat
Un cheval	A horse
Un poney	A pony
Un hamster	A hamster
Un cochon d'Inde	A guinea pig
Un serpent	A snake
Un lapin	A rabbit
Un poisson rouge	A gold fish
Une souris	A mouse

Now draw a picture of your own face next to the second speech bubble. Write about yourself in the same way that Stephanie has described herself.

✓ MUSIC

In Year 7, students will experience a wide range of musical styles from a variety of different cultures. Students work together, developing co-operative and social skills whilst composing and performing their own music. Keyboards and numerous percussion instruments are used in most schools; in some there will be a wider range of instruments. Individual lessons with instrumental teachers can usually be arranged if required. A charge is made for these lessons.

✓ DESIGN TECHNOLOGY

Within DT (sometimes called CDT) which is usually taught as Food, Textiles and Resistant Materials (RMT), students have the opportunity to use a variety of tools, equipment and materials in order to follow through ideas, which they have researched, developed and modified in the light of factors such as time available and cost. Design briefs (tasks) may range from the production of a model monster with moving parts, an original recipe for muffins, or a pattern for a fabric storage bag.

✓ ART AND DESIGN

Students are likely to experiment with a range of artistic techniques such as drawing, painting, collage, print-making, textiles and sculpture. (Note: in some schools not all these will feature in Year 7.) Students will use a variety of starting points before developing and improving their ideas, many of which will be recorded in their sketchbook. Students will examine work by well known artists, as well as their classmates, with a view to developing their own critical skills.

✓ PERSONAL, SOCIAL AND HEALTH EDUCATION (PSHE)   (Often called PSE)

Most schools' PSE programmes focus on ensuring a smooth move into a new school and on building a group identity and supportive ethos within a Tutor Group and Year Group. Study skills such as settling into an effective homework routine are likely to feature, as are activities designed to encourage mutual respect, tolerance and self-confidence. Issues relating to healthy and safe lifestyles will also be covered in this subject. Students will become well-informed about their rights and responsibilities as citizens in this country and some schools will teach CITIZENSHIP specifically. The work may include developing an understanding of conflicts and of the way the media can influence our views of the world.

✓ INFORMATION AND COMMUNICATION TECHNOLOGY

A certain amount of prior knowledge of ICT is expected of students starting in Year 7 and most will have already developed their basic skills. The programme in Year 7 is likely to include an introduction to the school's own ICT systems and network and many of the following activities: Desk Top Publishing, keyboard skills, word processing, research using the internet and e-mail, spreadsheets, presentation using Powerpoint, graphic illustration, practising systems control and creating a website.

✓ PHYSICAL EDUCATION

Students will improve their individual and team skills in a variety of sports, whilst developing their personal fitness. A key aim is to encourage enjoyment of participation in sport through the development of specific skills, techniques and tactics. Which sports are offered will depend to some extent on the facilities available in any particular school.

✓ RELIGIOUS EDUCATION

Students will study many aspects of religion and spirituality. They will be introduced to the major world religions as well as considering some of the 'Big Questions': Who is God? What is justice? What responsibility do we have to the world around us? Sacred texts will be introduced, as well as major religious figures and their teachings.